ALL I DID WAS ENTERTAIN A LITTLE ANXIETY...

BY

Sheila Dickinson

1994

ISBN 089716-521-7
Printed in the United States of America
FOR BOOK ORDERS CALL 1-800-517-7380

Cover design and illustrations by Suzanne Brooker.
Library of Congress 94-066785

10 9 8 7 6 5 4 3 2 1

PUBLISHED BY

PEANUT BUTTER PUBLISHING
226 SECOND AVENUE WEST
SEATTLE, WA 98119
(206) 281-5965

ALL I DID WAS ENTERTAIN A LITTLE ANXIETY...

To Jim, who has joy in his faith.

Picture a green house.

In front of the house
is a great big yard.

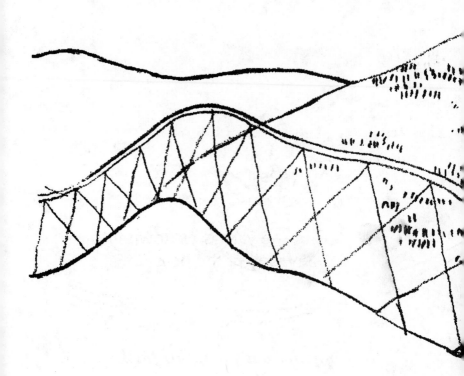

Below the yard is a fence.

And the yard dips down into
the valley of the Beasts.

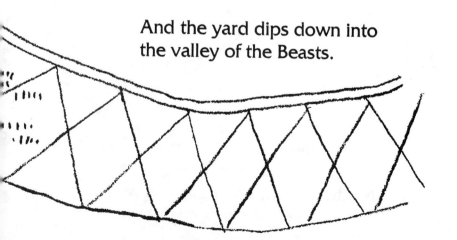

In the house the Father has placed the Growing Child, and given him food and heat and light and water and everything he needs.

The Father said to the Growing Child,
"Stay away from the Beasts, because
the Beasts are not for my children.
Have nothing to do with them."

Up against the fence we see a Beast.
He has white, fuzzy fur, and hardly
looks like a beast at all, except for his
sharp pointy ears and sharp teeth.
His name is *Anger*.

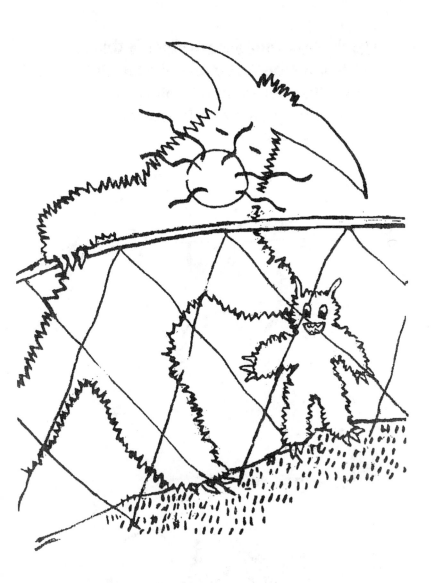

Behind *Anger* stands *Mother Resentment*. She is a great big, red, hairy Beast with hot breath.

Behind *Mother Resentment* is this enormous big, dark blue Beast with tremendous power and strength. His name is *Father Bitterness*.

Next is a fellow called *Diverse Lust.*
He is all green in color, with purple
jowls. He has bulging eyes, drools
a lot, and breath of fire. His skin is
curiously smooth and pleasant to
the touch.

He stands at the fence going back and
forth from one foot to the next. He's
always feeling, always feeling at the
top of the fence.

Beside *Diverse Lust* stand two little fellows that are almost identical to *Anger,* except they are gray in color. They have sharp pointy ears and sharp teeth. They are twins, and their names are *Depression* and *Anxiety.*

Behind the twins, *Depression* and *Anxiety,* stands their big brother, *Fear.* He is a great big, tall and skinny Beast. He has long, black hair, a great big mouth with lots of teeth, and long, black, skinny fingers with long, skinny arms.

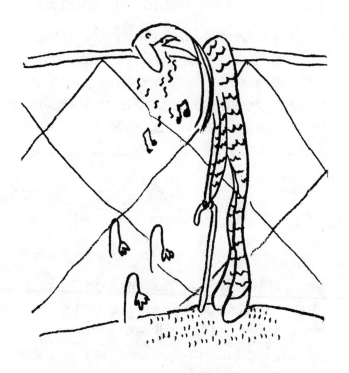

The last Beast at the fence is an old
man. His name is *Self-Pity*. He looks
so frail. His gray skin hangs off his
bones in folds. He has a few yellow,
slimy teeth and a few greasy strands
of hair. He sings the song "Poor Me,"
but the old man's foul breath is
poisoned.

The Father said, "Stay away from the Beasts. Have nothing to do with them. These are not for my children."

The Child, in the process of growing,
would go out and poke at the Beasts.

They would become
enraged and
try to climb up and over
the fence after him.

The Growing Child would
always get back to the
house in time.

The Father would say, "Stay away
from the Beasts. You don't know.
Stay away from them."

One night, Father looked down and
saw that the Child had grown to the
age of accountability. The Father
could no longer be a hedge against
the Child's willful disobedience,
so during the night Father
took down the fence.

The next day the Grown Child
decided to go out and poke at
Anger. He poked at *Anger* and
poked and poked.

Immediately, *Anger* came into the house! "Whoa!" How did you get into my house so quickly? It's different when you are right here up close! Ooh, boy! It's even more intense!"

The Grown Child poked
at *Anger,* and *Anger*
poked right back at him,
"Hmpfh! Argh!" The
Child really enjoyed
himself all day long.
"Oooh! This is soooo
good!!!!!"

When evening
came, the Grown
Child would not let
Anger go.

The next day the Child poked at *Anger* and *Anger* poked back at him. All the next day, they poked and poked, and finally there was a knocking at the door.

The Grown Child opened
the door, and in marched
Mother Resentment.

She walked through all the rooms of the house, and her hot breath made every room very uncomfortable.

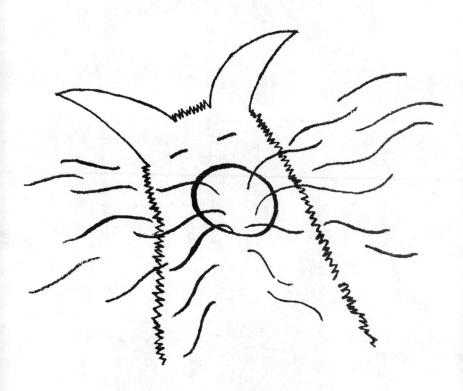

The Grown Child rather enjoyed the discomfort of her presence.

Three days after *Mother Resentment's* arrival, there was a banging at the door and in lumbered *Father Bitterness.*

At first, he went to the kitchen and
began destroying all the food with his
tremendous power and strength until
the food was covered with the ashes
of *Bitterness*.

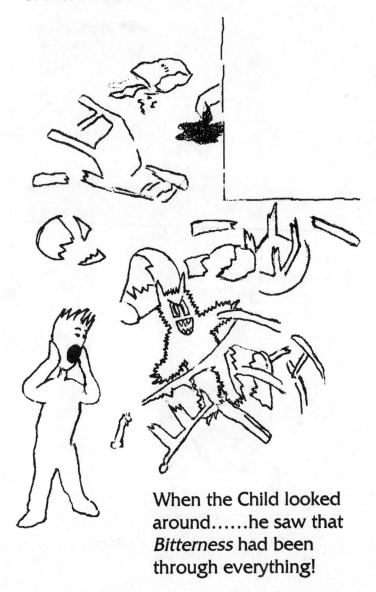

When the Child looked
around......he saw that
Bitterness had been
through everything!

He went to the bedroom and broke
down the bed. He went to the living
room and ruined all the furniture.

The Child called to
his friends, "Help!"
They came running.
"All I did was let in a little
Anger and keep it for awhile,
and now all the food tastes of
Bitterness and there is no place to
lay or sit in my house anymore,
because *Bitterness* has destroyed
everything!"

They gathered together and
beseeched the Father for strength.
Father did strengthen them, for they
were quiet and still before him.

Psalm 5

With all the strength of the Father,
they were able to push the whole
family of Beasts from the house.

The Father, seeing the Child's
willingness to be rid of the Beasts,
restored his home to order.
"Ahhh! That's better! I'll never!
I'll never do that again! Boy! Have I
learned my lesson!" the Child said.

A few months later, the Child was remembering how curiously smooth is the hide of *Diverse Lust.*

"Ooh, I think I will just go pet him."

Immediately, the green blob was in his house! The Beast started picking up things that did not belong to him, drooling all over them, and started fires with his breath in the most unexpected places! Oh, dear! Oh, no! Oh, my! The Child ran after the Beast trying to put the fires out, but it was too late! The Child could not keep up!

Soon, the Grown Child's whole house was on fire! "Heeelp!" The Child called his friends, and they came running. "This is an emergency!"

"I was only
remembering the past,
and I was just going to
touch this fellow.
Now my whole house
is on fire, and I can't
put it out myself!"

The Child and his friends asked for help. In the Father's strength, with all their heart, they were able to put out the flames for their friend, and push the Beast from the house.

Matthew 18:18-20

"Oh! Thank you! Thank you friends!" the Grown Child said. "When I was younger, I used to be able to touch that fellow, and it would not have that effect on me."

"As I have grown in the Father, it seems harder now. I see how truly strong the Beasts are, and how vulnerable I am. Oh, wow! I'm not going to do that again!"

Then one gray day, the Child looked out the window and there stood the twins, *Depression* and *Anxiety*. Their noses were pressed right up against the window pane.

Now the Father had said, "Stay away from *Depression*. It starts out with a bad temper, with the same look and feel of a tantrum. It makes everyone in your house suffer, because you are not having your own way."

Wisely, the Grown Child
went around *Depression*,
picked up *Anxiety*, and
brought him into the
house. Ooh, they rocked in
the chair all day, dum dee
dum dum. He played
with him and pulled
on his ears and
talked to his little
anxiety all day.

In the evening, there was a tapping at
the door. The Child walked to the door
and said, "Oh, that's your big brother
Fear." He opened the door a crack to
tell him he couldn't come in…

Suddenly, one of the long fingers of *Fear* came and wrapped itself around the Child's hand, and then another and another. The Beast had him so wrapped up, he could hardly move for *Fear*. (gulp) He could hardly breathe either.

Fear's great big mouth
was threatening to
devour him altogether.

"Help!" the scared Child
called to his friends,
"Help!"

They came, and the Child said,
"All I did was entertain a little *Anxiety*
all day, and now I can not move
because of the spirit of *Fear*."

They beseeched the
Father for strength, and in
the Father's strength, they
peeled the Beast from him
finger by finger and pushed
Fear out the door.

"Praise God!" the Child felt better, "You sure won't hear me calling you anymore! Oh, my goodness! Thank you friends! Thank you for standing with me!."

A long time later, the Child was
suffering from great despair. The
Grown Child weakly looked out the
window and saw the old man
standing in his yard, singing,
"Poor Me. Poor Me."

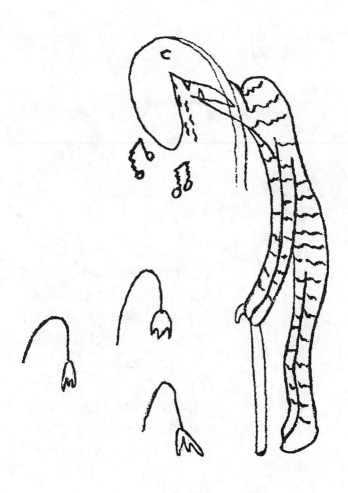

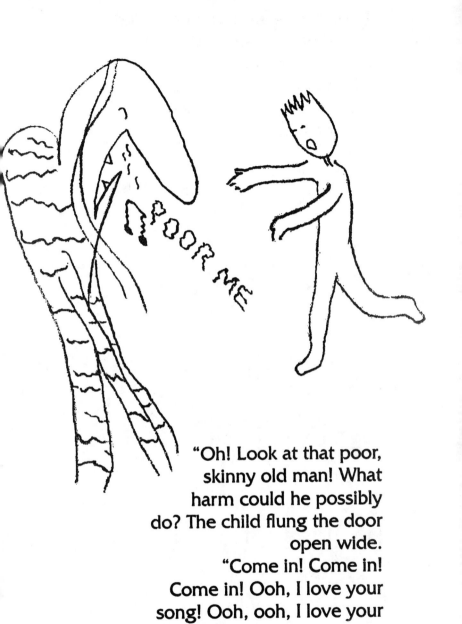

"Oh! Look at that poor, skinny old man! What harm could he possibly do? The child flung the door open wide. "Come in! Come in! Come in! Ooh, I love your song! Ooh, ooh, I love your song! Sing it to me one more time!"

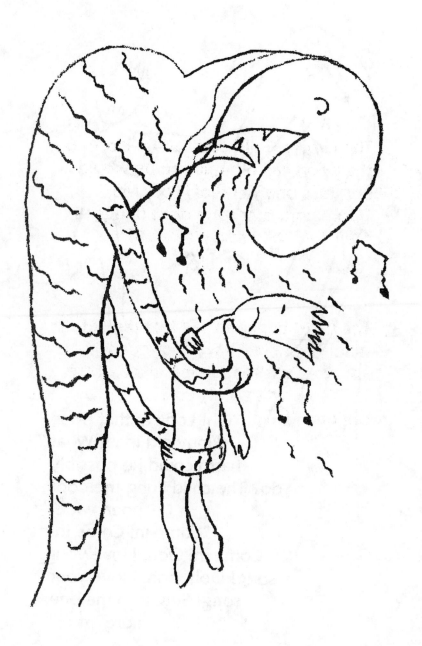

The Grown Child cuddled up close to
the poor, frail old man, so he would
not miss one word of "Poor Me."
"Ooh, ooh, that song does things to
me," the Child said, "I love it!
I love it!"

The Child began to see that the old
man's foul breath was poisoned,
and the Child's suffering grew worse.
The Child was barely able to
call out, "Help!"

His friends came, but they too were
charmed by the song, "Poor Me."
They said "Ooh! That's our favorite
song, too! We love it!"
They all sat around and listened to
that wonderful song.

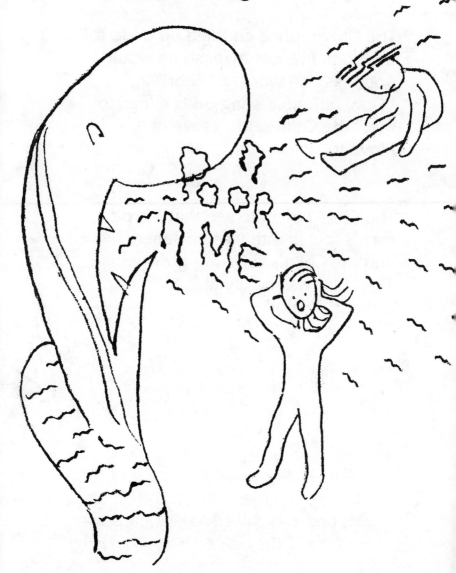

The Father looked down, and did
strengthen them. Of all the Beasts,
this one was the strongest, because
they loved him so much.

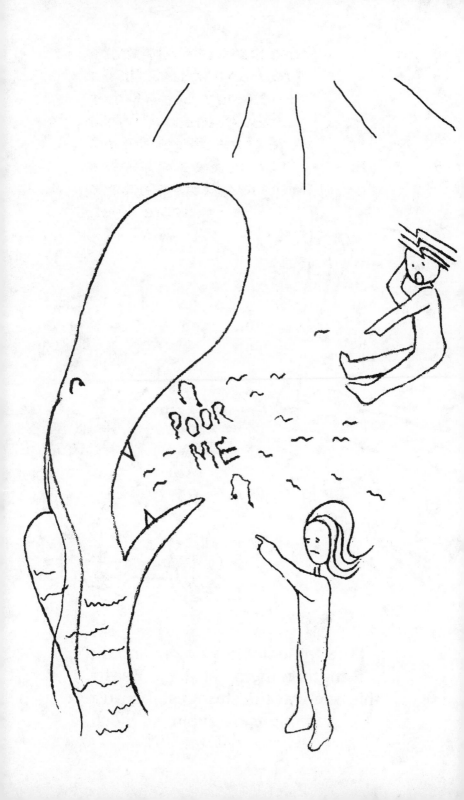

Those that were very strong
rose up and said, "In the
strength of the Father,
enough already!" While
some of the others whined,
"Oh, let him stay. Oh, let
me have that song just one
more time."

Finally, the strong were able to push the old man *Self-Pity* from the house.

Our Father has said, "When these Beasts are in our house, we can not see the Kingdom of God."
What is the Kingdom of God?

The Kingdom
of God is
Peace and
Joy.

Romans 15:13

When the peace
is gone, and the joy is gone,
chances are we are entertaining one
of the Beasts in the house.

"Thank you friends!
Thank you for caring and listening,
and for all your help.
In the Father's strength, there is hope.
Thank you for standing with me."

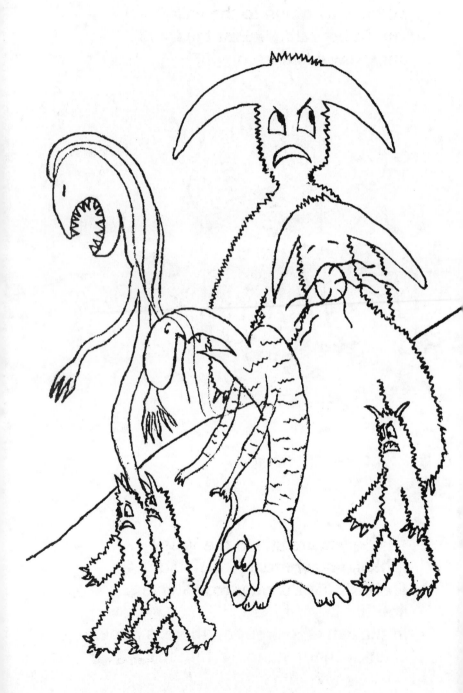

After awhile, the Beasts ambled
all the way down to the valley.
The Father said, "Resist the Devil,
and he will flee from you."

The Beasts are still in the Valley
to this day where you can find
them......if you want to.

James 4:7

ABOUT THE AUTHOR

Sheila Dickinson combines career and marriage. Together with her husband Jim, they own a restaurant in Kingston, Washington where Sheila performs as an actress.

Since 1978, Sheila has known and loved Jim's three children, John, Michelle, and Suzanne.